BOMBER'S MOON

Also by Mike Harding

Walking the Dales

BOMBER'S MOON

Mike Harding

MICHAEL JOSEPH
London

First published in Great Britain by Michael Joseph Ltd
27 Wrights Lane, London W8
1987

Set by Goodfellow & Egan, Cambridge
Printed and bound by L. Van Leer & Co. Ltd, Deventer, Holland.

British Library Cataloguing in Publication Data

Harding, Mike
    Bomber's moon
    I. Title
    784.3'05   PR6058.A/
    ISBN 0-7181-2963-6

CONTENTS

Foreword	vii
BOMBER'S MOON	1
THE ACCRINGTON PALS	5
ME AND MY FRIEND THE BOTTLE	9
CHRISTMAS 1914	11
KING COTTON	15
DANDELION DAYS	17
FOR CARLO	21
GOD HELP THE POOR	23
GOOD MORNING, MORNING	25
ME AND GRANDAD'S MATES	29
THE OLD GREEN IRON LAMP	33
JIMMY SPOONS	35
JINNY BOBBIN	37
LUCKY LEGS	41
THE MILLS OF THE VALLEY	45
MINERS IN THE RAIN	47
ON A SUNDAY	49
TO PASSING CROWDS	51
WAITING FOR ME PAY DAY	53
PLUTONIUM ALLEY	55
THESE POOR HANDS	57
SHADY LANE LADY	61
THIRTY NIGHTS	65
ON THE TOUCHLINE	67
THE WILD GEESE	69
A SMALL HIGH WINDOW	73
ROLLING HOME	75
Afterword	77

FOREWORD

The songs in this collection were all written between 1970 and 1985. They all have a story to tell, some of them about a particular person (such as 'Jimmy Spoons' or 'Jinny Bobbin'), others, such as 'The Accrington Pals' and 'Bomber's Moon', are about groups of people. Some, such as 'Christmas 1914', deal with historical events and a few, such as 'Good Morning, Morning', are just about themselves. They are mostly sad songs, not because I find life dismal or gloomy but because the events or people described struck me in that way. I often say that I didn't write these songs but that they wrote themselves. I think there's an element of truth in that insofar as the stories were already there, I just put them into words.

Some of the words you may find folksy; that is largely because my interest in music developed out of rock and roll, through blues into British and Irish folk music. I've tried not to be too consciously folksy in my writings but I have also tried to use language that I feel approximates to the mainstream tradition of folk poetry because I believe there is an element of starkness and truth within such poetry that gives it an everlasting quality rarely found in popular music.

If we're still around by then and the politicians haven't succeeded in wiping us off the face of creation, I believe that people in a thousand years will still be reading and listening to 'Barbara Allen', 'Bourgeois Blues' and 'The Foggy Dew' for the pleasure they give and the story they tell. But will any but social historians be listening to the oeuvres of Sigue Sigue Sputnik or songs like 'The One-eyed Purple People-eater?'

Many of my songs are anti-war songs for reasons which will become more apparent if you read the notes to songs like 'Bomber's Moon'. Politicians will tell you that nobody likes a war and then will glibly send thousands of young men and women off to die, claiming war as a necessary evil. But it's never the politicians who have to die. As Adolf Hitler said when he was told that thousands of soldiers a day were dying on the Russian front, 'That's what young men are for.'

So, these songs are about war, about work, about emigration and about love. I wrote these songs because the people themselves were often denied a voice. I wrote them because I was angry, because I still am angry that it is the little people all the time who get screwed, ripped off, exploited, worked to death and are asked ultimately to die for a country in which many of them have never owned, as Bernie Parry says in his song, "One Handful of Earth".

I'm not a Communist, I'm not a member of any political party. I reserve my right to dissent, to argue, to protest and to fight exploitation and ignorance wherever I see it, and I try to do it the only way I can, through song.

I guess I'm getting old you know. I
listen and I talk. And when I listen I'm
listening for silences: but when I talk I'm
full of grievous words.
      Studs Terkel (talking to Tony Parker)

I hate a song that makes you feel you're no good,
born to lose, bound to lose.
      Woody Guthrie

BOMBER'S MOON

'44 in Bomber County
Young men waiting for the night,
In the hedgerows birds are singing,
Singing in the falling light.
And the captain says, 'Tonight there'll be a bomber's moon,
We'll be there and back underneath a bomber's moon.
A thousand bombers over the northern sea
Heading out, out for Germany.'

Chalkey White stands at the dartboard,
Curly Thompson writes to his wife,
Nobby Clarke and Jumbo Johnson
Are playing cards and smoking pipes;
And over the hangers rises a bomber's moon,
Full and clear rising, as the engines croon
And the planes they taxi out on to runway five
And sail off out into the silvery night.

Sandy Campbell checks his oil gauge,
The Belgian coast is coming soon;
Curly Thompson lifts his sextant,
Lines up on a bomber's moon
And waves are shining there beneath the bomber's moon.
The Lancasters flying high beneath the bomber's moon
Coming in along the Belgian coast
A thousand silver-shrouded ghosts.

Flak flies up around the city,
Jumbo Johnson banks the plane,
Goes in low and drops his payload,
Turns to join the pack again.
And people are dying there beneath the bomber's moon,
The city's a raging hell beneath the bomber's moon,
And the planes head out towards the northern sea:
Young men coming home from victory.

Over Belgium came the fighters,
Flying high against the night;
Curly Thompson saw them coming,
Closing in before he died.
And the young men shot them down beneath the bomber's moon,
Shot them down in flames beneath the bomber's moon;
Young men sending young men to their graves
Saw them down into the North Sea waves.

1

Now it's '44 in Bomber County
Mrs White dusts the picture and she cries:
Chalky White in uniform
Looking as he did the day he died.
And for God's sake no more bomber's moons,
No more young men going out to die too soon,
Old men sending young men out to die,
Young men dying for a politician's lies.

For God's sake no more bomber's moons,
No more young men going out to die too soon,
Old men sending young men out to kill.
If we don't stop them then they never will.

No more no more bomber's moons
No more no more bomber's moons.

I've never been a fan of Bomber Harris and his thousand bomber raids on the cities of Germany. It's arguable whether they brought the war any nearer its conclusion and many historians maintain that, far from being beaten by the constant destruction and killing, the spirit of the German people for resistance was in fact hardened by the bombing. I do know one thing for certain, and that is that my own father, Lewis Arthur 'Curly' Harding, was sickened by the job he was being asked to do. He'd joined the RAF as a boy entrant just prior to the war and had eventually become a flight sergeant navigator in Lancasters flying from Lincolnshire. It was there that he had met my mother while she was working in the Land Army. They fell in love and married quite quickly and it wasn't long before I was on the way. On one occasion just before he was due to leave on a mission, he told my mother that he was heartsick every time he flew on one of the big raids because he knew that they were blanket-bombing civilian targets and that each raid was killing innocent women and children. As far as he was concerned, that had nothing to do with why he'd joined the RAF in the first place.

It is ironic that my father was killed on a raid on which he should never have been. He had finished his tours and was due to be grounded as an instructor, but when the squadron were a crew short for that final raid due to sickness, he and the crew of his Lancaster volunteered. He never came back, and he lies now with the rest of the airmen in a tiny graveyard in Holland in a row of simple graves that are tended by the local schoolchildren.

I tried to write this song for a number of years but for some reason it would never happen. I wanted to write it for a couple of reasons: one is that one of my best mates is a German called Jürgen Bock who was eighteen months old in Cologne, Germany, when my father died bombing his country; the other is that my mother, who was bride, widow and mother all in just over a year, has never really got over the scars my father's death left her with.

As a small child I sensed that my father's death was an area that my mother wouldn't talk about, so I grew up with a feeling of mystery and loss that I suppose will always be with me. Then, one night about four years ago now, I heard a radio programme in which a pilot who had flown Lancasters in the Second World War talked about what he called a 'bomber's moon', when the moon was full and clear in a cloudless sky. It was a double-edged sword for them in that it meant that the pilot and navigator could see the details of the landscape below, but also that the enemy fighters and anti-aircraft crews could get a clear visual on the plane. The phrase 'bomber's moon' stuck in my mind and as though it were the key that I'd been looking for for years the words of the song came pouring out on to the paper. I sat at the piano and I wrote the song in less than an hour, or rather, I should perhaps say that the song wrote itself. So, when people ask me now how long 'Bomber's Moon' took to write, I always say it took me an hour and a lifetime.

On the last British and Irish concert tour, we spent two nights in Lincoln and I went into the cathedral. In the RAF chapel there I found my father's name on the roll of honour, along with thousands of others. When he died, he was a smiling, fresh-faced 23-year-old from the apple towns of Devon. He died in a war against an evil greater than any the world had previously seen. But if it hadn't been for the stupidity and greed of politicians, that madness and evil would never have arisen. The gas chambers of Belsen were built with the penstrokes on that piece of paper in the railway carriage at Compiègne.

THE ACCRINGTON PALS

Smokey town where they were born
Down in the valley, smokey little streets;
They were pals from childhood days
Climbing trees and running through the fields
And they all played together
Through the turning of the years,
Sharing their laughter, sharing all their fears.
The seasons saw them growing, oh,
The seasons passing turned them round
Through the turning, turning, turning years,
The Accrington Pals.

Schooldays end, the lads all went
To work, some spinning, some weaving in the sheds,
On the land or down the pit,
Working hard to earn their daily bread.
And they all went walking up old Pendle Hill
On Sundays, the larks sang high above the dale,
Little Willie Riley
Played his mandolin and sang.
They were laughing, they were singing then,
The Accrington Pals.

1916 came the call:
We need more men to battle with the Hun,
Lads of Lancashire heed the call;
With God on our side the battle will soon be won.
So they all came marching to the beating of the drums
Down from the fields and factories they'd come,
Smiling at the girls who
Came to see them on their way.
They were marching, marching, marching away,
The Accrington Pals.

Blue skies shining on that perfect day,
A lark was singing high above the Somme;
Brothers, pals and fathers lay
Watching that sweet bird sing in the quiet of the dawn.
Then they all went walking out
Towards the howling guns,
Talking and laughing, calmly walking on,
Believing in the lies that
Left them dying in the mud;
And they're lying, lying, lying still,
The Accrington Pals.

Smokey town that heard the news
Down in the valley, smokey little streets;
Houses quiet and curtains drawn
All round the town, a silent shroud of grief.
And the larks were singing still above Old Pendle Hill,
The wind was in the bracken,
The sun was shining still,
And the larks were singing sweetly as
The evening fell upon the Somme
On Edward Parkinson
Bobby Henderson
Billy Clegg
Johnny Molloy
Norman Jones
Albert Bury
Willie Riley,
The Accrington Pals.

In 1916 the British Government, worried that the supply of men for cannon fodder in Kitchener's new army was drying up, instigated a brilliant new manoeuvre in the recruiting stakes. Reasoning that friendship between men has always been a strong factor in any group dynamics, they came up with the idea of forming Pals Battalions composed of men from the same towns and cities. Men who had played together and worked together, it was reasoned, would join up together. This, it was thought, would not only give them a greater loyalty to the regiment and to each other but would also encourage any shirkers who might doubt the worthiness of the cause to come forward, lest they be shamed by their pals.

Thus the great Pals Battalions were formed: the Leeds Pals, the Bradford Pals, the Hull Pals, the Durham Pals, the Sheffield Pals, the Barnsley Pals, the Manchester Pals. Accrington was the smallest town in Britain to raise a Pals Battalion. When it was found that the town itself had not quite mustered a complete battalion, volunteers came in from the small villages in the countryside around. The Mayor led the recruiting drive, addressing crowds personally on the steps of the Town Hall, pontificating on the justice of the cause and the glory of the battlefield, spouting out what the war poet Wilfred Owen called 'The old lie, Dulce et decorum est/Pro patria mori.' (Sweet and right it is to die for the Fatherland).

The generals were later to claim the Battle of the Somme as 'the brilliant advance of July the First'. The battleplan hung round the strength of the British heavy guns, which would pulverise the German lines. At this point the British frontline would quietly leave their trenches and simply stroll across No Man's Land to occupy the decimated German positions. But the Germans were so well dug in and so deeply secured that the bombardment, terrible though it was, did little other than warn them that an advance was about to take place. Had the British been allowed to advance running, at normal battle pace, the story might have been different. They were ordered, however, to walk across, which gave the Germans all the time in the world to climb out of their dug-outs and take up their positions in the machine-gun nests. As the British strolled towards them, one party kicking a football, they mowed them down like corn beneath a scythe blade. The Germans later confessed that they could not believe what was happening: their guns became red-hot and their machine-gunners had to relieve each other as their arms grew tired from the constant firing. And still the soldiers walked towards the guns.

That day, 100,000 men took part in the battle; 21,000 were killed and 35,000 wounded. Of the Accrington Pals, that battalion of 1,000 untried and unprepared men, 234 were killed and 350 wounded. Almost every family in Accrington had lost somebody. At first the Town Hall hid the truth, but as news filtered through via letters home from field hospitals and returned casualties, it gradually dawned that something terrible had happened. The people laid siege to the Town Hall, dragged the Mayor out and forced the news out of him. It has often been said, and I can believe it, that the little town of Accrington never recovered from that 'brilliant advance of July the First'. Among the 56,000 killed and wounded on that day there was not one general.

ME AND MY FRIEND THE BOTTLE

Me and my friend the bottle
We knew a thing or two,
Me and my friend the bottle
Knew that we'd get through
Just as long as we stayed together.

Me and my friend the bottle
Got through a load of money;
My old friend the bottle,
He made the blues seem funny,
Made sunshine of stormy weather.

CHORUS: *Come on, old pal,*
All things must pass
And the world looks better
Through the bottom of a glass.

Me and my friend the bottle
We used to fool around,
And my old friend the bottle,
He made me fall down,
Laugh and sing
The whole night long.

Me and my friend the bottle
We used to talk real good,
And I knew my friend the bottle,
He really understood,
Helped forget
When things went wrong.

CHORUS

Me and my friend the bottle
We fell out one night,
Me and my friend the bottle
Had a hell of a fight!
Oh, it nearly
Broke my heart.

You know my old friend the bottle,
He really brought me down,
Me and my friend the bottle
Together we almost drowned.
It's a shame
But the best of friends must part.

9   CHORUS

I think it must be the Irish in me. I like to have a drink or two, particularly in pubs if the music and the crack is good. The trouble is that one drink can lead to another and then another and before you know where you are you're not much good to anybody, particularly yourself, and what at the time sound like pearls of wisdom in the morning end up to be nothing but the paste gems of an idiot. I've said a lot of witty things while under the influence. I've also said a lot more stupid things. As hangover champion of several continents, and, as someone who once volunteered to punch a six foot four Scots Guard sergeant-major while stark naked stood on a bar in a mess in Germany, I think I know what I'm talking about.

CHRISTMAS 1914

Christmas Eve in 1914
Stars were burning, burning bright
And all along the Western Front
Guns were lying still and quiet.
Men lay dozing in the trenches,
In the cold and in the dark,
And far away behind the lines
A village dog began to bark.

Some lay thinking of their families,
Some sang songs while others were quiet
Rolling fags and playing brag
To while away that Christmas night.
But as they watched the German trenches
Something moved in No Man's Land
And through the dark there came a soldier
Carrying a white flag in his hand.

Then from both sides men came running,
Crossing into No Man's Land,
Through the barbed-wire, mud and shell holes,
Shyly stood there shaking hands.
Fritz brought out cigars and brandy,
Tommy brought corned beef and fags,
Stood there talking, singing, laughing
As the moon shone down on No Man's Land.

Christmas Day we all played football
In the mud of No Man's Land;
Tommy brought some Christmas pudding,
Fritz brought out a German band.
When they beat us at the football
We shared out all the grub and drink
And Fritz showed me a faded photo
Of a dark-haired girl back in Berlin.

For four days after no one fired,
Not one shot disturbed the night,
For old Fritz and Tommy Atkins
Both had lost the will to fight.
So they withdrew us from the trenches,
Sent us far behind the lines,
Sent fresh troops to take our places
And told the guns "Prepare to fire".

11

probably exaggerated but the point remains that the ordinary   British and German troops

And next night in 1914
Flares were burning, burning bright;
The message came along the trenches
Over the top we're going tonight.
And men stood waiting in the trenches,
Looked out across our football park,
And all along the Western Front
The Christian guns began to bark.

There are many who will tell you that this never happened or that if it did it was wildly exaggerated, but there are so many accounts of the incident in writings of the time that only the wilfully blind would doubt the truth.

The First World War has dominated my imagination since I was a child. The stupidity of all wars was here made doubly stupid by the ineptitude of leaders who were prepared to see men die in millions in the mud, facing each other across a few hundred yards of barbed-wire and shell holes. Two great industrial nations had strutted on the stage of Europe striking warlike postures for so long that when a crazed student assassinated the Archduke Ferdinand at Sarajevo it was too late for the fools to back down. And so the whole crazy steamroller got under way, supported as ever by the profiteers, the racketeers and the arms manufacturers.

Between 1914 and 1918 a whole generation was killed, gassed and maimed. Anzac troops were slaughtered at Gallipoli, Sikhs were blown to pieces on the Somme, Canadians were massacred at Verdun, Americans shot to bits at Passchendaele, volunteers from both the north and south of Ireland were killed in their thousands. And boys from villages and towns in every corner of England, Scotland and Wales were waved off at the station by mothers, wives and sweethearts never to return, of if they did they were often mutilated, gassed or shell-shocked so that their lives were ruined.

When you see the old men at the Remembrance Day services it's difficult to see them as the sixteen-year-old boys who lied about their age so that they could join with their pals in the Great Patriotic War. Like all wars, it produced heroism and courage on an incredible scale. While the fat brigadiers and generals were safe behind the lines, VCs and MCs were won by young boys and men facing the most unbelievable horrors.

The war produced an outpouring of literature, poems, novels and plays. The poems of Wilfred Owen with their quiet unsentimental concern that the truth be told contrast greatly with all the jingoistic trollop that was appearing in the *Boy's Own* paper and *Young England*. While the comfortable warmongers safe at home were hurrying the young men on to the troop trains, Owen was telling it like it was.

> *Bent double, like old beggars under sacks,*
> *Knock-kneed, coughing like hags, we cursed through sludge,*
> *Till on the haunting flares we turned our backs*
> *And towards the distant rest began to trudge.*

The Great War for Civilisation brought forth a whole body of literature from the poetry of men like Isaac Rosenberg, Siegfried Sassoon and Wilfred Owen to the accounts of life at the front such as Robert Graves's *Goodbye to All That* and Henry Williamson's *The Patriot's Progress*. But there was a sub-literature of the war, too, diaries and journals that were kept by the ordinary footsloggers and Old Contemptibles. They give a picture of life in the trenches from the viewpoint of the common soldier. These diaries and journals are tremendously valuable for their sheer immediacy and for the light they throw on the Old Sweats' way of life and death in the trenches. Three such journals that are well worth reading are *Old Soldiers Never Die* by Frank Richards, *The Bells of Hell* by Eric Hiscock and *Tom Green's Journal*, to be found in the Imperial War Museum (when, oh when are we going to have a peace museum?).

The story of the first Christmas of 1914 that inspired me to write the song was one I found in Frank Richards's book. The generals denied that it ever happened, fearful that the desire for peace might spread like an epidemic along the trenches, but the diaries and journals of the men who were there and the photographs that were taken on that historic occasion when men said 'no' to war and embraced their enemy prove beyond doubt that it did indeed

happen.

KING COTTON

See how the lint flies out over the moorland,
See how the smoke in the valley clings,
See how the slate roofs shine in the drizzle:
This is the valley where Cotton is King.

See how the houses cling to the hillside,
Hear how the streets of children sing,
Wake to the scream of the factory hooter:
This is the valley where Cotton is King.

See how hunger has eaten the faces,
Tired flesh to the bones just clings,
Dust in the lungs and the bodies are twisted:
This is the valley where Cotton is King.

Sleep is washed from the broken faces,
Morning clogs on the cobbles ring,
Off to the mill the weavers hurry:
This is the valley where Cotton is King.

You work all day to the loom's hard rhythm,
Scrabble and toil till your tired bones sing,
Then you crawl back home as the gaslights flicker:
This is the valley where Cotton is King.

This is the land where children labour,
Where Life and Death mean the self same thing,
Where the many must work that the few might prosper:
This is the valley where Cotton is King.

If you travel on the roads around what is left of Oldham and Rochdale, you will see why people have called it variously names such as Cottonopolis and Spindledom. In that great bowl made by adjacent spurs of the Pennines lie hundreds of mills, square-built and functional, their chimneys smokeless now, windows smashed. Many have been converted into storehouses, foam-rubber factories, or have been divided into offices, studios and light industrial units; many others are simply falling down or being pulled down. Fifty years ago there were four or five times as many mills: the whole area was one vast factory turning cotton from India, America and Egypt into raw goods that clothed the world.

As a youth I worked for a firm of boiler-scalers and travelled all over Lancashire climbing inside the massive boilers in the engine houses of these mills scraping the rust and scale off the insides of the boilers and crawling through hundreds of feet of flues out to the chimney bottoms, shovelling soot out towards the door in the foot of the chimney through which I could see the daylight streaming. The mills were dying then and the streets around were dying with them. Row on row of houses huddled like snakes along the hillside that had once housed working families now housed the unemployed.

I've never been one to believe much in the Protestant work ethic, the myth of the nobility of labour. I prefer instead to give credence to an old South American proverb: 'If work is all that good, why haven't the rich kept it all to themselves?'

If you stood in the yard at the end of the working day twenty years ago or so and watched the mill workers streaming out on their way home, you could see the effects of King Cotton's benefice in some of the people. There were many bonny mill girls and strong-looking lads, or course, but these were the younger ones. Amongst the older people, particularly the women, it was common to see the stunted growth and splayed wishbone-shaped legs that told of rickets and poverty.

When the First World War drew recruits from some of these northern towns the army medical officers were shocked at the poor physical development of the men they examined. They saw a generation of starved and stunted men offering themselves up for service. It was then that the famous Bantam Regiments were formed, the fighting cocks of the poor starved North.

Somebody once chided a mill owner on the poor standard of the houses he provided for his workers to live in. 'Nay,' he said pompously. 'The mill's for 'em to live in, the houses is nobbut to sleep in.'

It's hard to believe that in the latter half of the twentieth century cases of rickets and TB are reappearing again in the North of England.

DANDELION DAYS

Dandelion Days,
Laughing all the way
To the banks of the canal
Running through the grass,
Knee-high with my pals.
Oh, those Dandelion Days, oh,
Oh, those Dandelion Days.

Dandelion Days,
Jam jars for the tadpoles,
Sticklebacks and newts,
Kicking up the dust in our wellington boots.
Oh, those Dandelion Days,
Oh, those Dandelion Days.

CHORUS: *How did it come about that all our tomorrows*
So quickly turned to yesterdays?
And the innocence and joy have all gone skipping
Down the Dandelion Days,
Down the Dandelion Days.

Dandelion Days,
When I was the champion
Hopper in our street,
When I had a friend
That no one else could see.
Oh, those Dandelion Days,
Oh, those Dandelion Days.

Dandelion Days,
When the sun really shone
The whole summer through,
When there really was
A man in the moon.
Oh, those Dandelion Days,
Oh, those Dandelion Days.

CHORUS

Dandelion Days,
Running to the pictures
Satd'y mat'nee every week
In the tuppenny rush
Climbing over seats.
Oh, those Dandelion Days,
Oh, those Dandelion Days.

Dandelion Days,
Cheering all the goodiés
And hissing evil down,
Then screaming like the wind
As Hopalong hit town.
Oh, those Dandelion Days,
Oh, those Dandelion Days.

CHORUS

Dandelion Days,
Barefoot through the park,
Playing hide and seek,
Sailing matchsticks in the fountain.
Oh, those Dandelion Days,
Oh, those Dandelion Days.

Dandelion Days,
When Time went on tiptoe
Slowly passing by,
And Grandads lived for ever
And no one had to die.
Oh, those Dandelion Days,
Oh, those Dandelion Days.
Oh, those Dandelion Days,
Oh, those Dandelion Days.

CHORUS

This song is about innocence, those days that William Golding tried to explore in his novel *Free Fall*, asking the question when and where do we lose our innocence? The Satd'y mat'nee or tuppenny rush took place every week when legions of us kids would run through the streets to the cinemas on the main road where we'd sit in the plush seats screaming with laughter at Heckle and Jeckle and the Three Stooges and sit rigid with fear as the Emperor Ming threatened yet again to vapourise Flash Gordon.

I remember too that everything seemed smaller then, or rather that small things took on a magnitude of their own and matchsticks became sailing boats on their way out of the park to the great seas of the world. In those days it was still possible to see 'infinity in a grain of sand'. Where oh where did they go?

FOR CARLO

Every Sunday in summer he came in his van
And the kids all shouted, 'Here's Carlo the ice-cream
    man!'
Banging on doors as the van stopped and the bell
    rang
And dads in armchairs woke up as the kids sang:

CHORUS:
    Hey, Mam, give us some money for Carlo,
    Hey, Mam, give us some please before he goes.

He's got raspberry sauce, he tells us it's elephant's
    blood;
I don't think it is, but, Mam, it tastes real good.
He's got wafers, cornets, Ninety-Niners and twists,
Oh, get your purse, Mam. Come on, Mam, get it quick.

CHORUS

Every year when the Whitsun Procession came round
He'd walk with all the other Italians in town;
He carried the Madonna and gave us all a big smile
As the band played and the kids all cheered and went
    wild.

CHORUS

And now on summer Sundays I take my own kids
And we walk down that old street where I used to live.
I sit down in my dad's old chair in the house,
The bell rings and the kids come in and all shout,
And they say,

Hey, Dad, give us some money for Carlo,
Hey, Dad, give us it quick before he goes.
Hey, Dad, hurry up, don't be so slow,
Hey, Dad . . . All the kids they love Carlo.

When he first came to our street, Carlo Visci had a beautiful horse and cart and we kids would run out with a bit of apple or a piece of bread for the horse and some pennies for an ice-cream cone or a wafer or a 'twist' (a cone made with dark brandysnap-tasting pastry). His ice-cream was always homemade from eggs and tasted far creamier and much more wonderful than the modern Mr Runny's whipped water and emulsifier. Carlo rang a bell and shouted, 'Ice cream!' like all proper Italian ice-cream sellers should. He told us kids jokes and watched us growing up through the years.

Each Whitsun Friday the Roman Catholic churches in Manchester and Salford diocese would walk in procession to the city centre; it was wonderful to see the banners flying and hear the bands playing and the choirs singing. The churches with large Irish congregations like St Patrick's and St Malachy's would march past early on in the procession, while towards the end would come the Poles, the Ukranians and the Italians.

The Italians always carried great statues of the Virgin Mary on a litter surrounded by mounds of flowers. We kids would look out for Carlo and cheer him as he came up Market Street sweating under the weight of his load in his black trousers and white shirt. During all the years I knew him, his black hair never whitened and his smiling face never changed. His horse was put out to grass and exchanged for a new van as Carlo moved with the times, but for twenty-five years he came to our street laughing and joking with all the kids, his hair still black and his smile always the same.

This is for him, for all the 'elephant's blood'.

GOD HELP THE POOR

Going down the road with a hole in your shoe,
Ain't even got the money to booze away the blues,
It's the same old story, nothing's new:
God help the poor.

A hole in your coat, hole in your shirt,
You've got to wear a scarf to hide the dirt:
What you going to wear to hide the hurt?
God help the poor.

CHORUS:
For years and years they kept telling you
We need you;
Now the only place for you
Is down in the dole office queue.

You talk about the thirties, nothing's changed.
The same old people getting screwed again,
And the people at the top say they're not to blame.
God help the poor.

Fifteen years at the job that you did,
The boss he comes along and pulls away the skids;
Christmas is coming, what about the kids?
God help the poor.

CHORUS

You never was one to shirk a fight,
Knew what was wrong and what was right,
But now you're in the dark and they've switched off
    the lights.
God help the poor.

So you're going down the road with a hole in your
    shoe,
Can't even find the money to booze away the blues:
It's the same old story, nothing's new.
God help the poor.

CHORUS

Just before Emma, our second child, was born, I had a row with the boss at the place I worked because he wouldn't allow me a couple of hours off one morning to take my wife to the hospital. The row developed into a major battle and I lost my job, finding myself with another child about to be born and two weeks' wages to last me until I found another job.

I went down the Dole and signed on as unemployed. My employer maintained I'd left of my own will. I claimed that I was sacked. The point here is that it's not who was wrong or who was right but that the people at the Dole refused to allow me to claim unemployment benefit since they said I'd left the job of my own will. I was forced therefore to claim Social Security.

Anybody who has ever known poverty and the mindless faceless system, and the sometimes wilfully cruel and arrogant clerks who dole out the State's pittance, will understand how degrading and dispiriting it is to sit for hour after hour in a bare dirty room where the smell of unwashed bodies and cheap cigarettes mingles with babies' nappies and the sounds of crying children, coughing old men and the sighs of the hopeless. As you look around you in the Dole, you can see how the spirit can be beaten out of a people so easily.

It's all very well for people to talk about the scroungers in our society, the black economy, the dole fiddlers; it's easy to tell people to get on their bikes and go and look for work. Where?

I've been there and felt it and seen it. On the last week I was on the 'Nat King Cole', we had spent the little money we had by the day before I was due to draw the dole and there was no food and not a penny to buy it with in the house. I had three threepenny bits weighing down the pendulum of an old wallcase clock to make it work. Out they came to buy a tin of beans to feed Sarah, the eldest child; my wife and I went hungry.

You don't forget times like that and nowadays when I hear the well-fed and complacent talking about the 'shiftless and the scroungers in our society' it makes me very, very angry. There are people who abuse the system and cheat on the dole but what is their crime compared to some of the Stock Exchange frauds of recent times that have netted individual criminals millions? Shakespeare's *King Lear* came late to that realisation when he said:

> *Plate sin with gold,*
> *and the strong lance*
> *Of justice hurtless breaks;*
> *Arm it in rags, a pygmy's straw doth pierce it.*

GOOD MORNING, MORNING

I was up in the morning with nothing to do,
Ran down the street, got a hole in my shoe;
The sun was on the cobbles, I heard all the kids,
Cats sleeping quiet on the warm dustbin lids,
And they all said:
Good morning, morning.

Up through the park then to Paradise Hill
Where Time stands on tiptoe when the roundabout's still.
Dogs chasing paper and kids calling names
At the parkies who chase them and spoil all their games,
And they all said:
Good morning, morning.

CHORUS:
> *Morning wakes to the smell of bread*
> *From bakehouse window panes,*
> *The sound of traffic growling through the town,*
> *The rattling of the trains,*
> *The smell of smokey bacon and hot sweet tea,*
> *The sound of a playground full of kids.*

Faces at windows, fingers at doors,
Seagulls that sing and buses that snore,
Schoolgirls with satchels and wind-blown hair,
Red-faced policemen and old ladies who stare,
And they all said:
Good morning, morning.

A sea full of chimneys points to the sky,
Down the street women hang washing on lines,
Grannies with cushions are sat on their steps,
And grandads with pipes and scarfs round their necks,
And they all said:
Good morning, morning.

CHORUS

Down through the market where work is all done
The iron and glass shine out warm in the sun,
Wind blows the papers and scraps down the street
And ties them in tangles round everyone's feet,
And they all say:
Good morning, morning.

Down to the river to watch the world pass,
Faces that hurry like sand through a glass
Into the city their wages to earn
And me without a penny but a million words to burn,
And they all say:
Good morning, morning.

CHORUS

When I was growing up in the early sixties everything seemed possible. There was plenty of work about and a lot of excitement in the air. Films like *A Taste of Honey, A Kind of Loving, Billy Liar*, and *The L-shaped Room* had seemed to point a way for working-class writers' voices to be heard.

I fancied myself as a bit of a poet and storywriter then, and when I was sixteen years old or so I would roam the city all night soaking up its atmosphere staying up until dawn streaked across the sky between the office blocks and warehouses, talking about Life, Religion, Politics, Art, everything and anything, with tramps and drunks, intellectuals from the university and drop-outs who were wandering the world just for the sake of keeping moving.

I was a great one for playing wag from school and I used to love 'sagging off' from my classes, wandering the art galleries and the museums and parks all day, then staying up in some all-night café talking to the characters there until the morning came, when I would wander off, imagining I was in a novel by Zola, walking through the city and down to the market as all the stalls and baskets were being cleared away.

I'd wander down to the river to watch the sun rise over its greasy slack length remembering the opening paragraphs of Joyce Cary's *The Horse's Mouth*, then I'd watch them coming into the city – the warehousemen and clerks, the shop assistants and pen pushers – and I'd vow that the 'toad work' would never get me. Of course it did in the end, but not for long. I may work harder now than I've ever worked, but at least I'm my own man.

This song was written in the mid-seventies, about the sheer joy of being alive in the awakening coolness of a summer's day that you know is going to be hot and cloudless and that you wish would go on for ever.

ME AND GRANDAD'S MATES

Grandad takes me fishin' on a Saturday,
Me and Grandad's mates.
Grandad brings me maggots, pink and yellow ones,
And me hooks and weights.
We fish all day come rain or shine
On the banks of the old canal;
Sometimes we say nowt,
Other days we chat away,
'Cos me and Grandad's pals.

Grandad takes me walking with his little dog,
He calls her Gyp.
We go to the pub and Grandad has a pint of grog,
Gives me a sip.
He says he drinks beer 'cos his legs are stiff
And it oils them and makes them supple;
Sometimes I think it works too well
'Cos it doesn't half make him wobble.

Grandad he comes round and sits with me
When Mam and Dad go out,
We play snakes and ladders and Monopoly.
Grandad has a bottle of stout.
He lets me stay up till half-past ten,
And if me Mam asks him what time
He made me go upstairs to bed,
Grandad says half-past nine.

Grandad tells me all about the things
He did when he was a lad,
Grandad tells me all about the war
And when things were bad.
Sometimes he talks about my Gran
And then he looks far away;
He says she's been gone a long, long time
But he'll see her again some day.

Grandad shows me tricks with pennies,
Grandad flies my kites,
Grandad brings me fish and chips
Home from the pub at night.
And if ever I grow up and I get old
And my kids they have kids,
Then I'll take 'em fishin' and do all the other things
That my Grandad did.

My grandad was away in Liverpool for most of my childhood working as a tailor in the city, sitting crosslegged on a table making suits for the shipping owners and merchants of the city. We saw him at Christmas and Easter when he would appear large and booming at the door with a nose like an elephant's trunk shouting in his loud Dublin accent, 'And how are yez all?'

I had a sort of substitute full-time grandad in my Great Uncle Bobby McGlaughlan, who was a gentle bespectacled pipe-smoking man who took me out for long walks through the fields and cloughs around his house pointing out the flowers and the holes made by moles and rabbits as we walked along. We went fishing on Bury Canal and on the mill lodges and reservoirs near his house. Uncle Bobby and Aunty Kitty lived at Besses o' th' Barn between Manchester and Bury. There was a golf course at the back of the house while down the lane was Prestwich Clough and the Philips Park Estate.

Looking at it now with the M62 motorway snaking through it, it seems very small indeed, but to me then it was the real countryside and I loved going to stay there during the summer holidays with my brown paper parcel of clothes. I'd stay there all the summer having 'adventures', although it was probably no more than five miles away at the most from my home in Crumpsall. I can still remember every station on the electric line from Crumpsall to Besses: Bowker Vale, Heaton Park and Prestwich. I counted them off eagerly each holiday, my nose pressed against the window as I watched the hot streets slide past until the maroon and cream sign read Besses o' th' Barn.

Uncle Bobby and Aunty Kitty were lovely people and kindness itself. He never talked down to me and always seemed interested in my childish prattlings. He told me a lot about his life in the Magnolia Street area of Manchester and about his days in the Merchant Navy on the Nova Scotia run. He read a great deal and I remember that his was the first house I'd ever seen with a bookcase full of books. He read lots of books by Patrick McGill and Jack London and as a socialist of the old school, when socialist had not been turned into a dirty word, he had fought the Fascist Mosley's brownshirts on the streets of Manchester.

I think all children should have grandads like my Uncle Bobby. We often used to get into trouble together. Uncle Bobby liked his pint and one hot summer afternoon while I was fishing on a part of the canal bank that just happened to be right beside a pub called The Jolly Bargee or some such, Uncle Bobby got a bit tiddly and we both got shouted at by my Aunty Kitty: him for getting drunk and me for letting him, although what an eight-year-old boy was supposed to do to stop a grown man having a drink I'll never know.

Uncle Bobby had a beautiful intelligent black labrador called Vic and once when I was staying with them I fell into a steam while playing and caught a cold. That night while I was in bed I overheard my Aunty Kitty tell Uncle Bobby that she was going to rub Vick (an ointment used for treating coughs and colds) on my chest. When my mother phoned up to ask how I was enjoying my stay 'in the countryside' I said I wanted to go home.

'Why?' asked my mother.

'Because they're going to rub the dog on my chest,' I cried.

THE OLD GREEN IRON LAMP

At the corner of our street there was an old gas lamp
And us kids used to meet there every night;
We'd swing from its old bars and we'd play hide and
    seek
In the shadows just beyond its yellow light.

CHORUS:
    And it must have seen some meetings and some
       changes through the years;
    I bet it's seen some laughter and I know it's seen
       some tears,
    But Time's hurried on and that old gang has gone
    That met beneath that old green iron lamp.

All the kids in our street gang would meet each night,
Swop comics, just tell jokes or fool around.
We'd talk about the things we'd do when we grew up
While the light from that old lamp spilled on the
    ground.

CHORUS

I wonder where they are, the kids in our old gang,
Now that all the years have come between.
We've all changed and we've all travelled and that
    old lamp has gone
And nothing's going to be the same again.

CHORUS

If I could bring those old days back I wouldn't even try —
There were times when we knew trouble and knew
    pain,
But I know I'd give a lot to bring back our old gang
And meet them underneath that lamp again.

CHORUS

The street I lived in during all my growing years was a typical northern industrial town terrace of red-brick houses with slate roofs, lace curtains and outside lavatories. The street was cobbled and the street lights were gas lamps of the old style with four square glass-paned heads, gas mantles and stumpy arms that stuck out for the lamplighter to rest his ladder on when the mantle wanted changing or the lamp wanted cleaning.

We weren't allowed to play in the house except on the coldest of nights so the hours between tea time and bed time (in the North, tea is what you have when your dad gets home from work) were spent playing in the street. The lit pool of pavement below the gas lamp near our house was an obvious meeting place and it was there that we'd play our games and make up plans for expeditions to Heaton Park, the Saturday cinema or the far-off wilds of Ashworth Valley.

I can still remember the nicknames of some of my pals from those days. 'Andy' was Jimmy Hands, Barry Wharfe became 'Wharfie', and as such has featured in more than a few of my stories about childhood, not always I'm afraid with a total dedication to the truth. 'Flea' was Geoffrey Lee and 'Big Weed' and 'Little Weed' were the two Heywood boys, one of whom was tall and thin and the other short and fat.

The girls didn't seem to have nicknames and if you tried to give them one they were quite likely to give you a hefty crack. In those days the girls could punch nearly as hard as the boys and one family of sisters from the next street to ours were well feared for the solidity of their thumps. I remember being so winded by a stomach punch from one of them (she was about twelve and I was ten years old or so) that I thought I was going to die. Years later I saw her in high heels and stockings looking very ladylike on the arm of some young man going off to the pictures. I could hardly believe it was the same female thug that had nearly killed me.

JIMMY SPOONS

Down the long city streets on summer afternoons
There walked an old man, they called him Jimmy
  Spoons.
Times that I remember, me and all the other kids,
We followed him the long, long day through.

CHORUS:
  Hey, Jimmy, won't you play one more tune,
  One of those you learnt across in France.
  Hey, Jimmy, won't you play just one more,
  Play one so the little kids can dance, nah, nah, nah,
  Play one so the little kids can dance.

Played his old mouth organ and his spoons they beat
  out time,
All the kids they followed him, he didn't seem to mind.
Times I often wondered why he was just a tramp
And where he went when the long hot days were
  done.

CHORUS

All the medals that he wore shone in the sun,
Memories of the trenches and a war that was long
  gone.
Now he was no soldier, just a dosser out of luck,
Living in that hostel on the hill.

CHORUS

Somewhere out in France a shell had torn his mind,
Left him burnt and broken, wearing rags, wearing a
  smile.
What happened in the trenches, in the mud and in the
  tears,
What happened to your life, Jimmy Spoons?

CHORUS

Down the long city streets I walk past my old home,
I've seen some changes now that I have grown.
Still you hear them singing on a summer's afternoon,
You hear the kids all saying to Jimmy Spoons:

CHORUS

When I was a kid growing up in Manchester we lived not far from a Salvation Army hostel for down-and-outs. One of them used to call at our house regularly for a cup of tea and became the subject of a poem that I wrote years later called 'The Sally Dosser Man'. Another was Jimmy Spoons.

Jimmy, dressed in cast-offs, unshaven and tatty-haired, played the mouth organ with one hand and the spoons with another as he busked the queues outside the picture houses along the main road near where we lived; the Globe, the Shakespeare, the Temple, the Premier and the Greenhill.

He'd returned from the First World War shell-shocked and had been unable to hold a job down ever since, so he'd taken to the roads as a tramp and had eventually ended up living at the Salvation Army hostel, a 'Sally Dosser Man'.

All the kids used to follow him along the streets as he played such tunes as 'Tipperary', 'Lily Marlene' and 'Pack Up Your Troubles'. He didn't seem to mind us following him. In truth, I hardly think he knew we existed. I remember he would stop occasionally and with a lost far-away look in his eyes would play a slow tune such as 'There's A Long, Long Trail A-winding' or 'Roses are Blooming in Picardy'.

I had forgotten all about Jimmy until I went back to Manchester in the early 1970s. It was a foggy December day just before Christmas. The Greenhill cinema had been turned into a bingo hall by then. but outside, playing for the coppers that folk threw in his hat, was Jimmy, isolated in the fog and lit by all the Christmas lights. Twenty years on and still playing.

JINNY BOBBIN

Born on a Friday in a cotton shed,
A pile of warp was my birth bed.
Work was scarce and she'd little pay,
She was back at the loom the very next day,
And she called me Jinny Bobbin.

When I was five I went to school:
Earn your bread was the golden rule.
The shadow of the mill was laid
Across the school yard where we played,
And they called me Jinny Bobbin.

When I was twelve I went in t'mill,
A skip with bobbins I'd to fill;
Through the dirt and the noise I was growing still,
I was small but I did it with a will,
And they called me Jinny Bobbin.

At eighteen I'd four looms to keep,
I paid me way from week to week
Till I met me lad as I danced one May
And he danced and he danced me heart away,
And he smiled at Jinny Bobbin.

We were walkin' out for more than a year,
Times were good, we'd nowt to fear,
Till I found meself in t'family way
And I wed me lad on a bright summer's day,
And he smiled at Jinny Bobbin.

Three bairns came with the passing years,
Then the war turned smiles to tears.
The lads came marching back from France
But my lad lay where he'd no more dance,
Far away from Jinny Bobbin.

I was forced to work in t'mill again,
I'd a lad and two lasses to keep by then.
Times were rough but we kept goin',
Paid our way and nothin owin':
She was proud, was Jinny Bobbin.

In '39 when t'second war came
Just like his father me lad went away,
He wrote me letters all during t'war
But after 'Cassino he wrote no more
And he left his Jinny Bobbin.

Now I work in t'mill and me lasses, too,
They've bairns of their own so they have to do;
And I look back on the time that's done
And I wonder where the years have gone
Through the life of Jinny Bobbin.

For I mind the days when times were hard
And dust lay thick in the old mill yard
And I think of the faces that I've seen
All passed away like a morning dream,
Through the life of Jinny Bobbin.

And I often think of the friends I've known
Who've lived out lives much like me own.
So there's me story and I know it's not much
But I could tell you of many a thousand such
As have lived like Jinny Bobbin.

For I was born on a Friday in a cotton shed,
A pile of warp was my birth bed,
Work was scarce and she'd little pay,
She was back at the loom the very next day,
And she called me Jinny Bobbin.

My history teacher at school always used to say that each of us has at least one book they can write and that one book is the story of their lives.

When I wrote this song I had in mind a woman who lived in the next street to us who had worked in the mill all her life and had seen her sons grow up and go to war to be killed in battle in a foreign land. Her daughters, like those of Jinny Bobbin, grew up to work in the factory, too, and her life and the lives of so many other working women made the base of a song which tells the story of not just one life but many.

It was the women of the North who held the home together, made do with what little they had and often went hungry so that their children and husbands might eat. In the working-class North it was hard to tell who suffered the most, the men who were often condemned to half a century of hard graft and little pay and who generally only lived to draw a couple of years of their pension, or the women who struggled and fought to bring up and feed their families often in the most degrading conditions and who yet managed to keep their homes neat and clean and their children fed and healthy. I think it was often the women who ultimately suffered the most.

I made up the name Jinny Bobbin from the jinny gate, a part of the loom, and the bobbin, which weavers insert into the shuttle to carry the weft between the warps, but, as the song says, there are 'many a thousand such' that have lived lives like Jinny Bobbin's.

LUCKY LEGS

In a one-bulb room in a one-way street
He opened up his eyes,
He saw the pale light in the gloom,
His mother heard him cry.
In a one-chance town on a luckless day
He was born through his mother's pain
While outside the posters in the street
Were peeling in the rain.

CHORUS:
A maze of ways and hazy days, Lucky Legs kept running,
Small-time chancer, big loser, didn't see what was coming,
Lucky Legs, Lucky Legs.

In streets along the dockyard wall
He learnt the creed of the city:
Dog eat cat, don't turn your back,
Take and show no pity;
Despise the weak, never show the other cheek,
You'll only get one chance.
Small-time crooks were his only books,
They taught him how to do life's dance.

CHORUS

And as he grew to better things,
Lucky Legs made his mark;
Sleek and black as an alley cat,
He was king of the dark.
His face grew scars like frosty stars,
He always carried a gun;
In the dawn of the day he hid away
From the cruel light of the sun.

CHORUS

And Lucky Legs they called him then
As down the nights he ran,
A tearaway afraid of the day,
But he was a drowning man.
A small-time strutting midden cock
Who didn't know the day was late,
While around him in the darker dark
The bigger foxes lay in wait.

41   CHORUS

In a one-way street in a no-chance town,
A shotgun found its mark
And took him apart like a rain of knives
Just on the edge of dark.
Only the death of a small-time loser,
His mother heard his scream of pain
While the posters in the city streets
Were peeling in the rain.

CHORUS

As a street kid growing up in Manchester I got to know many small-time villains. Some of them were harmless enough and some of them were real monsters. A lot of their macho talk about 'jobs' and 'shooters' and 'wheels' was sheer bravado, but some of it was true and petty crime in one area I lived in was the way of life, if not of the street, then certainly of the regulars at the corner pub.

There was one small-time villain who was different from the rest. He was clever but frustrated. He saw the good things in life and wanted them but didn't see any other way of getting them than by crime. Put to other uses, his intelligence could have been creative. Instead, he turned to the fast and easy buck. He did more time inside than he did out, so he can't have been all that clever, I suppose, but he did get mixed up with some very heavy members indeed. 'Persons', such as Damon Runyon might have said, that were 'definitely injurious to the average Joe's health'. Lucky Legs is a name I made up, but is no stranger than 'Jimmy Swords', the real name of one of the more famous members of Manchester's 'Quality Street Gang'.

'Lucky Legs' is in prison at the moment so, as you can see, the song is not based on a true life story. However, when he was arrested he was only one step ahead of a very heavy team of big-time villains who were out, if not to kill him, then at the very least to make a mess of him. I just hope the story doesn't come true.

THE MILLS OF THE VALLEY

These were the mills of the valley,
Wren's Nest, Egypt, India, Victorious and Hawk,
And these once proud mills of the valley
Are remembered only in the old men's talk.
Along the street the wind blows the dust,
The lodges are dry, the gates are thick with rust.
Small birds fly in the mill through broken panes
And weeds grow straggling in the empty lanes.

These were the mills of the valley,
Cromer, Turk, Raven, Clough and Bell,
Silent they now stand in the valley
And live on only in the tales they tell.
The barges lie sunk down in tangled reeds,
The lock gates are rotting covered in moss and
    weeds,
The old men stand on corners looking round
At the empty mills that loom above the town.

These were the mills of the valley,
Shiloh, Monarch, Heron, Marlborough and Delft,
And now through the towns of the valley
The shadows and the shell are all that's left.
On quiet days up on the sunlit moor
The echoes of the clattering looms still roar,
And from the lanes and through the empty streets
The wind sounds like a million hurrying feet.

When I was working on the buses in Manchester, the longest runs left Manchester centre for the outlying cotton towns of Rochdale and Oldham. The number 59 bus on the Oldham run followed a particularly long route going out beyond the town of Oldham itself to the village of Wren's Nest. I was a conductor, or 'bus guard' as they were known in the North, and so on days when the route was less than busy I often found myself with time on my hands, stood on the rear platform of the bus watching the world flash by us. Mill after mill slid past like tall ships riding at mooring above the slate roofs.

One summer's day, while standing on the platform, my arms wrapped around the bar watching the industrial landscape passing before me, I noticed how every mill that we drove by had its name emblazoned in huge letters, usually of white brick, either along the chimney or across the red-brick front, often on both.

I started making a note of the names and noting too something that was by then (the mid-sixties) becoming obvious to everyone: that the cotton mills and their towns were doomed, they were losing their old industry and it was doubtful if anything was going to take its place.

When the G Mex Centre was opened in Manchester on the site of the old Central Station, I was asked to perform in concert there with the Hallé Orchestra. Carl Davies arranged this song for full orchestra and one of the greatest memories of my life will be of that night as I sang 'The Mills of the Valley' to a packed hall with the whole orchestra playing behind me, only surpassed by the finale as I played the 'Radetsky March' on the bones with full orchestral accompaniment. They're a great band but I don't think I could afford to take them on the road with me.

MINERS IN THE RAIN

Faces hurry through the city streets,
Christmas lights are shining at their feet.
Above the streets the bright windows of a train
And the miners, miners in the rain.

Standing silent as evening cloaks the town
Stood collecting from the passing crowds,
City workers hurry home again
Past the miners, miners in the rain.

CHORUS:
Sons of miners, sons of miners, sons,
There was nothing else that could be done,
Whether you lost or whether it was you won
You went back on your feet and not your knees.

Families at home are living day to day,
There's not much left to lose for them to take away.
So they're standing because that's the only way
For the miners, miners in the rain.

For twelve long months they carried on the fight,
Not for pay or profit but for what they thought was
    right,
They fought on through the poverty and pain,
The miners, miners in the rain.

CHORUS

Now round the pit heads the men stand idly round,
Village are dying as the pits are closing down,
And in my mind's eye I see them in the town,
The miners, miners in the rain.

CHORUS

I think arguments about the wrongs and rights of the miners' strike of 1984–5 will rage on for years, but there is no doubt in my mind that what we saw was an act of bullying carried out on communities by a government using the police to carry out their policies.

Any arguments about ballots and union-bullying are fatuous in the light of the Coal Board's deliberate ignoring of closure procedures. They and the Government wanted a showdown, it was as simple as that. The tragedy of it all is that the people who suffered the most were the men and women of the mining villages and towns who saw their communities being destroyed. Mining is a hard and dangerous job and some of the pit villages had paid for their pits with death and blood for generations. To allow them no say in their own futures was not just undemocratic but ultimately immoral. Where were the accountants during the mining disasters? How do you put a price on miner's lung?

I was on a concert tour during much of the strike and I could hardly believe that I was living in a democracy when time after time we were stopped and interrogated as we made our way in the car along the motorways to concert halls in the Midlands and the North.

On the second night of a series of concerts in Sheffield I was having a pint with the roadies before the show in a little pub round the corner from the City Hall. That day the miners had started to return to work and were shown on the pub TV marching into the pits with heads and banners held high and brass bands playing. It was a sad day and doing the concert that night was one of the hardest things I've ever had to do. Nearly two thousand people had come out for a laugh and I just didn't feel like laughing. Ironically, the only other time I've ever felt like that was on the day John Lennon was killed when I was appearing at the Free Trade Hall, Manchester, in a concert for some miners killed in a pit disaster.

When I was filming a series for the BBC in the Appalachian mountains a couple of years back, I came across an old miner called Nimrod Workman. He was in his nineties and had been a coal miner and union organiser all his life. He'd been threatened, beaten up, shot at for his beliefs, and on one occasion his house had been burnt down.

'I see you got that MacGregor guy over in England now,' he said. 'You want to watch that guy, he's the guy who brought the state troopers in against the striking miners in Kentucky.' I passed on this news in a letter to the *Guardian* not long after the strike began and can only take the fact that MacGregor didn't deny it as assent.

I wrote this song about two miners who collected money for the miners' families relief fund outside the shops near my office in Manchester during the strike. They were there day in, day out, in fair weather and foul. I got to know them quite well during the strike and often stopped to have a bit of a crack with them.

I remember one night in particular, a wet windy night when the Christmas decorations had just gone up in the city and they were collecting from the homeward-bound office workers. The shining pavements were coloured by the Christmas lights and silhouetted against all the finery in the shop windows were the two miners in the wintry rain, sticking it out until the last hurrying worker had passed. I wrote this song for them.

ON A SUNDAY

'What do you think you are doing here?'
Asked the brass-faced man in the blood-red suit
With the medal ribbons hanging from his shoulder.
'It's not my fault but you can't stand here,
It contravenes the bylaws and it's against the regulations.
Don't ask me why, I've just got a job to do.'

CHORUS:
> *For there's no smiling, no smiling on a Monday,*
> *No laughing, no laughing on a Tuesday,*
> *No singing on a Wednesday, no dancing on a Thursday,*
> *No breathing on a Friday, no living on a Saturday,*
> *And on Sunday, yes, on Sunday no loving at all.*

'Little boy, you can't fish here,'
Said the plus-four legs in the Harris Tweed voice
To the small boy standing by the river.
'Don't you know that this river runs
By courtesy of Lord Muckybrass and God and all His angels?
Don't look like that, I'll confiscate your smile.'

CHORUS

'I'm sorry but you can't live here,'
Said the brick-faced man with the cast-iron hands
And the weight of plans and profits on his shoulder.
'We'll have to move you out of here
And bulldoze your dreams and pull down your hopes
And leave your memories smouldering in the rubble.'

CHORUS

'We can't have lovers lying here,'
Said the clay-faced man with his crow-black eyes
And the shotgun neatly nestled in his shoulder.
'Get up and get dressed and get out of here;
You'll scandalise the crops and frighten all the cows
And besides it's free and no one makes a profit.'

CHORUS

'These mountains aren't for you to walk,'
Said the gilt-faced man with the marble eyes
And the pension fund wrapped warm around his shoulders.
'We're going to blanket them with trees,
Plant grouse and deer, move farmers off, fence people out
And lock the crags and valleys in our bank vaults.'

49   CHORUS

There's a line often quoted in connection with the great enclosures of common land that took place in the eighteenth and nineteenth centuries and it's worth quoting here:

> *They hang the man and flog the woman*
> *That steals the goose from off the common,*
> *Yet leave the greater criminal loose*
> *That steals the common from the goose.*

Plastered all over the roadside in the beautiful Trough of Bowland in Lancashire are signs saying 'Private Keep Out', 'No Right of Way' and 'Private Land'. The Duke of Westminster owns it, the richest man in England. He keeps it as a grouse moor and for a few days in the year, parties of the rich and powerful are driven in Land-rovers on to the moor to blast small birds to Kingdom Come. Ordinary mortals are denied access to the hills in case they frighten the birds. Well, there you go – walking frightens the birds but blasting them to pieces doesn't!

I've grown tired of rules and regulations that forbid you to walk here or picnic there or fish there. I don't believe in invading anybody's privacy but how much of the land do some people want? I'm sick of watching people being pushed around by planners and developers, I'm sick of watching architects and politicians destroy communities for their high-rise plans and to suit their schemes.

I wrote this song in the mid seventies and decided that I wanted a photograph to illustrate it. So I went down to the local council yard where there was a vast collection of signs, old and new, saying 'No Entry', 'No Ball Games', and such things. As I raised my camera a 'jobsworth' came running out of a nearby council hut. He was obviously a watchman of the 'a spell in the army would sort you long-haired weirdoes out' kind.

'What d'you think you're doing?' he asked.

'I'm taking a picture of those signs,' I said.

'Oh no you're not,' he said. 'Not without permission you're not. You'll have to write to the Town Hall if you want to take pictures of those signs. What d'you want pictures for, anyway?'

I told him I'd written a song about the mindless stupidity of authority and particularly of jobsworths like himself. I also told him where he could stick his signs – so there you go, Nature imitating Art yet again.

TO PASSING CROWDS

I ate my heart out
On city pavements, I was a kid.
Night after night bright city lights,
Singing my song to passing crowds.

I learnt to read there
All of the faces I'd meet on the street,
A one-man show in a rainbow neon glow
Singing my songs to passing crowds.

CHORUS:
Old Benny the paper seller said,
'Someday, kid, you'll be a big star,
Big spender, good clothes, flash car.
But here's my word and don't forget it,
Here's my word and don't regret it:
You can get anything you want
If you give up enough to get it,
If you give up enough to get it.'

I took my chances,
Got off the pavements, I was The Kid.
Fought my way on to the big stage, on to the front
   page,
Singing my songs to passing crowds.

I learnt the ropes then,
Took all the chances over the years,
And yet on my way up things started to break up:
I lost my way in passing crowds.

CHORUS

My name's in lights now
Above the city pavements, the kid's made it big.
But when the crowds have gone home I'm still alone,
Watching them passing, passing crowds.

Last night I saw him
Outside the theatre, he was just a kid.
Hungry and cold, growing up, growing old,
Just a kid with a guitar dying to be a star,
Singing out his heart to passing crowds.

I've never taken show business seriously: without either a manager or an agent I've somehow managed to do the things I've wanted to do without compromising myself too much. Yet all along the line I've seen people so hungry for the tinsel and glitter of success that they'd almost kill for it. I've seen men brown-nosing TV producers and seen sub-standard comics grow rich on gags and songs they've ripped off from other performers. Some of it's made me mad and much of it has made me sad.

This song isn't autobiographical, it tells the story of someone I once knew who made it and of someone who didn't and who stayed as a busker outside the theatre in the neon lights.

One day I read that he had killed himself and the only reason I can think for him doing so was that he had become depressed by what he saw as his failure and lack of success. He shouldn't have done because he was a smashing songwriter and performer, but I think that in the end all the defeats just made him terribly lonely and he shut the door on the world.

There was no one there to open the door for him.

WAITING FOR ME PAY DAY

When I left school at Bobbin Hill
I went half-time at India Mill,
Pushing a skip from morn till neet,
Running about on nimble feet,
Waiting for me pay day.

Buzzers blowing through the street,
You hear the rattle of clog-shod feet.
Knocker-up shouts, 'It's Monday morn
And Dad's best suit is bound for t'pawn' –
Waiting for pay day.

Tally man is on the knock,
Workin' his way along the block.
Off wi't'gas and shut the door,
We can't pay him any more:
Call again on pay day.

Work is rough and pay is bad,
Tackler nearly drives you mad,
When I hear the buzzer blowin'
It's only pay day keeps me goin',
Waitin' for me pay day.

Wakes is comin' very soon,
No more workin' at the loom,
No more clockin' on for me,
We're off to Blackpool and the sea.
Hurry up next pay day.

We're cotton folk, a cotton town,
And cotton pays for Sarah's gown.
Works is hard and pay is poor,
There must be more to life I'm sure
Than waitin' for next pay day.

This song was written for a show called *In The Shade of the Old Arris Mill* presented as a late-night show at the Contact Theatre, Manchester, in the late sixties. It's built up from stories my mother told me of life in Collyhurst before the war and from conversations with mill workers in Blackley and Middleton, particularly in two pubs called The Old House at Home and The Ring O' Bells, places where I did my first singing in folk clubs. I always look on the song as the memories of three generations of cotton-town dwellers crystallised into one life.

Tally men were the men who ran clothing clubs whereby a housewife would 'buy' clothes for the family from specified shops and pay the tally man on the never-ever system. The housewife was encouraged to keep using the system so that in reality she was never out of debt. A similar system was run at many of the corner shops where the housewife would run up a 'book' and pay off as much as she could each pay-day Friday.

Tacklers were the skilled men who 'fettled' the looms when they broke down and who also got them ready for weaving particular patterns of weave. For some reason, they were scorned by the rest of the workforce, perhaps because they were rumoured to have a ready eye for the lasses.

'Tacklers' Tales' pointing out their stupidity were common. One tells of the tackler who dragged the mangle up into the bedroom to mangle the curtains. Another tells of two tacklers coming home drunk and deciding to sleep out the night on a building site. They used drainpipes as pillows. In the morning the first tackler complained that he hadn't slept a wink all night because the pillow was too hard.

'I were allreet,' said the other. 'I stuffed mine with straw and slept like a babby.'

The tune I used for the song is the tune to a well-known children's skipping song, 'Oats and Beans and Barley'.

PLUTONIUM ALLEY

When the hands that turn big business
Are the same that hold the gun
And the same that crack the whip,
Just to watch the little man run.
When the hands that hold the winning hand
Are the same that load the dice
And the fingers on the button
Have tied the old school tie –

CHORUS:
> Then fight, my friend,
> And fight them for all that you're worth!
> Fight them for you and for those that will come
> And fight them for all of the Earth.
> Fight them for the fields and the rivers,
> Fight them for the hills and the valleys,
> And fight them for the right to be born
> Away from Plutonium Alley.

When the rain that falls upon the land
Falls hotter than the lies
From the lips of politicians
Who've poisoned Paradise;
When the beaches and the mountains
Are poison-glowing dumps
And men stand by the electric fence
With their hands upon their guns –

CHORUS

When the profits and the power
Are running every game
And lies have called the poison
By an ordinary name;
When the fence is built up higher
And the midnight walkers come
To silence all your voices
With the truncheon and the gun –

CHORUS

During a Border Television debate on nuclear power held at their studios in Carlisle in 1986, I was howled down by the Friends of Sellafield and the workers of Sellafield and a senior Labour spokesman for daring to suggest that a nuclear accident was possible. After the show I asked him to give me a simple answer, a categorical yes or no and not a politician's fudging and lies to the question, 'Are you prepared to pursue a nuclear policy knowing that we are leaving behind a terrible waste that we have no way of dealing with for future generations to have to deal with?' He said 'yes' and I said a few things to him that I don't regret at all.

A few months later, the tragic consequences of Chernobyl left the nuclear power lobby with a thick plastering of egg on their chins, which they've since spent a lot of time, money and public relations expertise trying to wipe off. I don't think it's worked because Chernobyl and its aftermath has alerted a great number of ordinary people to the very real dangers of nuclear power.

It hasn't made one iota's difference to the politicians or scientists, however. Sizewell B is going ahead and there are plans for major new reactors to be built throughout the country, including a new PWR at Hinkley Point.

If nuclear power stations are all that safe, why don't we build them in the hearts of our major cities? How safe is the 'low-level dosage of radiation' that we're being permitted to receive? Why are there (and the CEGB now admits this) recognisable clusters of childhood leukemia around some of the nuclear plants? Just what is the connection between Sellafield and nuclear weapons?

So many questions; so few answers. We have hundreds of years of fossil fuel left that can now produce cheaper and cleaner power than nuclear power, giving us enough time to develop renewable forms of energy such as water, wind and wave power and geothermal sinks. What is the world going to do with the deadly waste byproducts? The whole thing would be laughable if it were not so tragic.

'Gasoline Alley' was the title of an American comic strip of the thirties. I thought 'Plutonium Alley' an apt title for the not so comic strip of the eighties.

THESE POOR HANDS

These poor hands hewed coal down your pit,
Felt the pick's savage kick
As it split the ebony gold in shattered flints.
These hands have held the flyers, the soft-mouthed whippets
And the breast of her who waited at the pit-yard gate.
Too late for where are they now,
Folded across his dead breast,
These poor hands, these poor hands.

These poor hands hauled on frozen ropes
Where black ice cut like knives
As the net spewed out a wave of silvery light.
These hands have held the pints and the whisky chasers
And the smiles of women his brass has bought in foreign ports
Almost without thought; but where are they now?
On the seabed fish swim through their grasp,
These poor hands, these poor hands.

These poor hands held the twirling spools
Where the nodding, flashing bobbin
On the loom wove out a many-coloured coat of dreams.
These hands have cradled bairns, soft-haired bairns,
And held the breast that plugged his sleeping mouth
As she dreamed his future out.
Now they're knocking on the parish door,
These poor hands, these poor hands.

These poor hands held the leather trace,
Turned the plough like a sea ship's bough,
And turned out waves of clay a furrow long.
These hands have held the growing and the dying of the year
And the hands of those who waited in the evening sun
When the long working day was done.
Now they're rotting in a Flanders field,
These poor hands, these poor hands.

These poor hands made a world from stones.
Now they lie, sea, land and sky,
Hands that reach out through the dreams of forgotten years.
These hands have held the knowing and the loving times,
Seen life grow and seen it die and a world pass by,
So the work of days and hands is done
For each and every one
Of these poor hands, these poor hands,
These poor hands, these poor hands.

I was working in a cotton mill in Rossendale with a boiler-scaling firm, and as we drove into the mill on the first day of the contract, I saw on the timekeeper's office wall a placard that just said 'HANDS WANTED'. It struck me then how working people had been seen as nothing other than a pair of hands to be bought, sold and sent down the river at a moment's notice.

Years later, I wrote this song in which I've used four people – a collier, a weaver, a fisherman and a ploughman – to represent the millions and millions of men and women who were often seen as nothing other than a pair of hands.

Bertolt Brecht said it all beautifully, in his poem 'Questions from a Worker Who Reads':

Who built Thebes of the seven gates?
In the books you will find the names of kings.
Did the kings haul up the lumps of rock? . . .

The young Alexander conquered India.
Was he alone?
Caesar beat the Gauls.
Did he not have even a cook with him?
Philip of Spain wept when his armada
Went down. Was he the only one to weep?
Frederick the Second won the Seven Years' War.
Who won it with him?

Every page a victory.
Who cooked the feast for the victors?
Every ten years a great man.
Who paid the bill?

So many statements.
So many questions.

SHADY LANE LADY

Shady Lane lady, you hide from the light
In the doorways of the night.
Shady Lane lady, watching the fast cars
Driving slowly by,
Oh, the Shady Lane lady, she smiles,
Sadness in her eyes.

Shady Lane lady, hearing the stories
Of all those troubled minds,
Puts on a smile she'll wear for a while
As she pulls down the blinds.
Shady Lane lady, she smiles,
Sadness in her eyes.

CHORUS: *You've heard all the stories,*
Of all the past glories,
The passions done and spent.
Faces have passed
Like sand through a glass
As they took your love and went,
Took your love and went.

Shady Lane lady, queen of the darkness,
Selling love for gold,
Will there be any left from so many
When all the love's been sold?
Shady Lane lady, she smiles,
Sadness in her eyes.

Shady Lane lady, with your sad magic
Standing through the night,
Midnight madonna, you hide in the shadows
As the city comes to light.
Shady Lane lady, she smiles,
Sadness in her eyes,

CHORUS

Shady Lane lady, giving some warmth
To the lonely and the lost,
Magdalene of the shadows, the only real sorrow
Is that we all give our love for a cost.
Shady Lane lady, she smiles,
Sadness in her eyes,
Shady Lane lady, Shady Lane lady,
Shady Lane lady, Shady Lane lady.

61

When I was in my late teens in Manchester I read a lot of books by the American writer Jack Kerouac and saw myself as one of the characters in *The Dharma Bums*, a sort of Zen Buddhist, Japhy Ryder character travelling the country searching for enlightenment in 'the alleys of the howling night'.

The sixties were a good time for indulging those sort of fantasies. Cities were fairly safe places at night and people would readily give you lifts as you hitchhiked about, so I spent a lot of time hitching up and down to London and other places, sleeping on people's floors, writing songs and poetry and worrying my mother. She was convinced I would turn out no good – I think she still is.

One night in an all-night café in Manchester I ended up talking to a woman a little older than me who belonged to the world's oldest profession. She had a lot of stories to tell, some of them funny, some of them sad, but what struck me as a common thread through all of them was the terrible loneliness of that twilight world where love is something to be bought and sold.

We talked through the night and as morning light stole over the old warehouses and banks of the city we went our ways. It wasn't until years later that I wrote this song. I don't find prostitution either disgusting or immoral. I just feel that it is ultimately sad.

THIRTY NIGHTS

I'm just sitting here in the dark,
A stranger in your city,
And as the room gets darker
Even the whores begin to look pretty.

CHORUS:
Going home,
It's time I was going home.
Going home,
Each night away the road back home gets longer.

Thirty nights of travelling round,
I begin to feel weary,
Even the lights of this old town
Are looking dim and dreary.

CHORUS

Sitting in this hotel bar,
Trying to keep myself warm,
The tables are dirty, the food is cold,
But it's any port in a storm.

CHORUS

Faces pass in my empty glass,
The room is going round and round,
Another bottle, another cup,
Another night in this one-horse town.

CHORUS

Theatre smells and Crest Motels,
Each night I feel a bit older.
What am I going to do if she comes
And puts her head on my shoulder?

CHORUS

One night in Scunthorpe in the middle of a sixty-date tour I stood on stage at the Civic Hall with a terrible bout of 'flu wracking my whole body; I had laryngitis, pharyngitis, tonsilitis and roaditis and I was trying to be funny to a hall full of people. Nobody who has never tried it will ever understand what that's like. Any other job on earth you can have a day off. Even the Pope can cancel a gig!

But in theatre the last people a performer ever lets down is 'the Public', as they're known, so it was on with the motley and out with the funnies. A couple of hours after that gig, while on my fortieth large brandy and hot water (for medicinal purposes of course), I wrote this song out of terminal self-pity. I soon got over it.

ON THE TOUCHLINE

CHORUS: *There's a man on the touchline*
Waiting to see what the score will be,
And that man on the touchline
Looks more than a bit like you and me.

Oh, that man on the touchline
Saw a village burn in Vietnam,
Saw bloodstains dry on a Belfast street,
Saw a pit heap slide in Aberfan.
Oh, that man on the touchline
Saw children die for a bowl of rice,
Saw farmers burn good corn and wheat
Just to keep up the market price.

CHORUS

That man on the touchline
Sees families live like frightened rats
In cold dark rooms with broken windows
Staring out above the railway tracks.
Oh, that man on the touchline
Lets the land be fenced and walled,
Watches them poison the fields and the seas
Knowing that the land is for us all.

CHORUS

That man on the touchline
Sees the jackboots polished up again,
Hears them marching through the city,
Tries to pretend it's only rain.
Oh, that man on the touchline
Watches the politicians cheat and lie,
Pretends he doesn't even see them
As they bungle and blight all our lives.

CHORUS

Oh, we stand on the touchline,
Watching through our TV screens,
Watching the world play deadly games
Little knowing what they really mean.
How much longer on the touchline
Before the game involves us all
And you find that the one who makes the running,
It's not you, it's the bloody ball?

67   CHORUS

I wrote this song some time in 1978 and recorded it on an album also called *On the Touchline* early the next year. I don't know if songs have ever toppled governments or brought about changes in society. Hitler didn't send many singers, or comedians for that matter, to the gas chambers. But I think that songs are at the very least a way of binding people together, of making them feel less alone perhaps; they are a way of telling the truth, and bullies are always frightened of the truth.

That's why the fascist dictators of Chile killed the singer and songwriter Victor Jara. They imprisoned him, with five thousand others, in the football stadium in Santiago after General Pinochet and the military had overthrown the elected government of Allende. Jara was a folksinger and songwriter who had come from peasant stock and who had written and sung songs of the people all over the country. He was seen as a subversive and was taken to the stadium during a series of swoops carried out against intellectuals and writers.

In the stadium with his guitar he led the prisoners in singing songs of freedom, so the captors broke his hands with their rifle butts to stop him playing the guitar. He carried on singing unaccompanied, leading thousands in song, so they took him out and murdered him.

I know that today many of us feel helpless in the face of great power and corruption and none but a fool would claim that the world is being led by honest or wise men. But enough small voices when they come together can add up to a mighty shout, and the one thing politicians are afraid of is people. It took Bob Geldof to show the world that it can get off its backside and do something really big. If only we could fight for peace in the same way that we fought for the hungry.

In the meantime, as the Quaker song says, 'How Can I Keep from Singing?'

This soldier is a member of the Army of the Republic of Vietnam. He said that he had killed two Vietcong women

THE WILD GEESE

My name is Michael Sheehan,
From Wexford town I came,
I walk the streets of Broadway,
Nobody here knows my name.
I worked upon my father's land
Till I could work no more,
Then I went to find a better life
On far America's shore.

CHORUS:
Oh, the wild geese are flying,
Oh, the wild geese are flying.

I've a brother out in Chicago,
Another in Montreal,
A sister a nurse in London town,
Another in St Paul.
My father and my mother
Are growing old alone,
Their children spread out across the world,
Many thousand miles from their home.

CHORUS

We're crossed the whole world over,
Half built it with our hands,
But our hearts and minds look ever back
To our homes in that far-off land.
We've worked wherever work was there
And when the work was done,
We've sat us back and had the crack,
The music and the song.

CHORUS

We've built your canals and railways,
Made buildings reach the skies;
We've fought wars for a stranger's cause
And on foreign fields we've died.
Like the wild geese, we've been flying
Across the restless waves,
In strangers' lands we've made our homes,
In foreign soil our graves.

CHORUS

And often times it's lonely
And you wish yourself back home,
Amongst your friends and family,
No longer forced to roam
Down the streets and in the bar rooms
In the town from whence you came,
Amongst those old familiar ways
Where everyone knows your name.

CHORUS

For my name is Michael Sheehan,
From Wexford town I came,
I walk the streets of Broadway,
Nobody here knows my name.
When I think about my family,
I think back on those times
I watched the wild geese winging free
Across those northern skies.

CHORUS

The Irish came to be given the name 'The Wild Geese Nation', after those Irishmen who went to fight as mercenaries in foreign wars, usually against the British. My family on my mother's side came over from Ireland in the early years of this century and settled in the Collyhurst and Ancoats areas of Manchester. The O'Neils and Pynes were originally from Wexford and Dublin and came to England, like many other Irish before and since, because they were looking for work.

My family has all the Irish traits of heavy drinking, a tendency to depression followed by bouts of euphoria, and an ability with words and music that seems to be in the blood. My grandfather was a great storyteller. My great grandfather was a fiddler. My uncles could all sing and play the mouth organ, my grandmother sang rebel songs to me on her knee when I was a child, and family parties always had some element of music and tale-telling in them.

I have always had a special love for Ireland, for her people and her music, and always felt that Ireland has a special place in my mind. A mate of mine, Michael Sheehan, who came originally from Killorglin, County Kerry, gave me the idea for this song one day when in a pub I looked at him and saw in his black hair and dark brooding face the story of my own family and millions of others driven from home to live restlessly in a stranger's land.

Go into an Irish pub on a Friday night when there's a session on and you'll hear music and singing whose roots go back into Celtic prehistory. Ireland's changing now, dragging itself into the twentieth century with a vengeance: the little thatched cottages so beloved by returning Americans like Ronald Reagan are fast being displaced by an epidemic of bungalows with long drives and crested gateposts. I can't help wondering if together with the poverty and inequality the essential magic might not also have been lost.

A SMALL HIGH WINDOW

There's a small high window where the sun comes in
And it falls and makes a rainbow in the puddles on the floor
There's a small bird singing in the broken pane
And how I wish, oh, how I wish that I could fly
Free as that bird out to the moor.

Oh, it's every morning I get out of bed
And my mother has my dinner packed and ready in my bag,
And my father says school's over, you must be a man,
And the whistle blows, the whistle blows,
The day begins, the hammers clang.

CHORUS: *Fly away*
Oh, fly away, little bird,
Fly away, oh, fly away, little bird,
On freedom's wing
Out to the moor.

Now my schooldays over I must go to work
And see my friends still playing in the sunlight in the street,
Then it's over the croft and through the steelworks gate.
Oh, but it's hard, oh, but it's hard
To feel the shackled chains about my feet.

And I work all day in dark and dust and noise
Where the hammers smash the steel and rock the world
    beneath my feet,
And shining men move through the forges' gloom
Like shadows burnt, like shadows burnt
Out by the fiery steel.

CHORUS

But when Sunday comes and there's a week's work done,
Then I take our dog and walk the old paths up on to the fell,
And for all that day then I am freedom's king
And I can dream, and I can dream and hear the larks,
Sing freedom's song above the dale.

There's a small high window where the sun comes in
And a small bird comes for crumbs that I throw for him
    on the floor.
Then he flies through a shaft of sunlight through the
    broken pane
And how I wish, oh, how I wish that I could fly
On freedom's wing out to the moor.

When I worked as a boiler-scaler in Manchester, we were sent one week to scale the boilers at British Steel, Gorton. The whole area was dominated by a huge steelworks and a nearby locomotive building works, Gorton Tank. I think I remember that the streets around were called Vulcan Street and Bessemer Street and that the nearby pubs were called The Vulcan and The Forge, but that may be just my fancy.

We were working in one of the huge sheds where red-hot steel was forged into the shafts for giant turbines by banks of massive drop-hammers that let hammers the size of bungalows fall on to the steel, smashing out storms of sparks that flew across the sheds. I palled up with a lad there about my own age who, like me, was mad on cycling and camping and hill-walking. Each dinner time we'd sit and talk about hills we'd climbed and places we'd cycled. The boiler-scaling job was only a temporary one for me and I'd told him that I was going to get out of it and do something else with my life. At the end of the week, when we were leaving and packing the wagons up with our gear, he came out to say goodbye and just said, 'You're going now. You're getting out of this place. I'll be stuck here for the rest of my life.'

This song is for him.

ROLLING HOME

We've been on the long road and the story's near told,
Night after night and show after show.
A one-night-stand band travelling the land,
Now it's time to be rolling home.

CHORUS:
Rolling home, rolling home,
Now the night's over it's time to be gone.
Rolling home, rolling home,
It's time to be rolling home.

We've seen the day break, seen the moon on the Lakes,
Crawled through the fog going over the Snake,
Been tired and been crazy, hungover and hazy,
Now it's time to be rolling home.

CHORUS

We've been so many places, seen so many faces,
Made new friends, met old friends, head-bangers,
   head cases,
And we've sung through the night, even got a bit tight,
Now it's time to be rolling home.

CHORUS

We're been up, we've been down, we've loonied
   around;
Just like the circus, we've come to your town.
But the night's hurried on and it's time we were gone,
Time to be rolling home.

CHORUS

So, come one and come all, the parting glass calls,
May your pleasures be many and your sorrows be
   small
And I'll raise up my beer, wish you good luck, good
   health and good cheer,
For it's time to be rolling home.

CHORUS

I've been on the road as a musician since my late teens; since the early seventies I have travelled the world from North America to the Indian Ocean, from Northern Ireland to Australia, giving concerts in everything from four-thousand seater concert halls to tin huts in the Australian Sandy Desert.

I often finish a show with this song because it says something about life on the road and about what has happened in that concert hall that night. It's a song I always like to dedicate to the roadies, those unsung heroes of the touring world who rig the lights and the sound and who are there a long time after the party's over, clearing up the mess and stacking the van ready for another night in another city.

Although I do a one-man show, on the 1987 tour of the UK and Eire I carried twelve and a half tons of sound, light and instrumentation that travelled in an artic. and tractor. There were seven roadies in a crew bus and myself and my driver/road manager – truly a circus coming to town.

So this song is for Davy, Craig, Gordon, David, Steve, Nigel and Jimmy, not forgetting Jack, Doris, Nobby, Robbo, Big Ged, Groge, Hugh, Hedgehog Pie and the Brown Ale Cowboys. Thank you, gentlemen.

AFTERWORD

I would have liked to have printed the music together with the words of these songs, but for various reasons that is impossible. There are, however, two albums that contain some of the songs in this book: *Bomber's Moon* (MOO3) and *Plutonium Alley* (MOO9), both on the Moonraker label.

I want to thank here all the people who consciously or unconsciously helped to make these songs and to thank in particular Sally my editor, Sandie, the designer, and Pat and John who did such a great job on the illustrations.

ACKNOWLEDGEMENTS

The author and publishers are grateful to the following for permission to use photographic and printed material on the pages given here: 2, 4, photographs taken from CECIL BEATON – WAR PHOTOGRAPHS 1939/45, courtesy of Jane's Publishing; 6, 8, 20, 22, 28, 34, 42, 46, 74, courtesy of the Salford Local History Library; 10, reproduced courtesy of Magnum Photographs, photograph by Leonard Freed; 12, EYE DEEP IN HELL – LIFE IN THE TRENCHES 1914-1918 by John Ellis, © Imperial War Museum; 18, 26, Crown Copyright, reproduced with the permission of the Controller of HMSO; 30, 32, 72, A PHOTOGRAPHIC MEMORY, © Jack Hulme, published by Yorkshire Arts Circus; 36, BBC RADIO TIMES, photograph by Barry Bevin; 38, taken from WORKTOWN PEOPLE by Humphrey Spender, photograph © Humphrey Spender in association with Tom Harrisson Mass-Observation Archive, published by Falling Wall Press, reproduced by permission of Curtis Brown Ltd; 40, 52, 58, © BBC Hulton Picture Library; 44, 62, taken from THE SECRET PARIS OF THE 30s, © Madame Brassaï, published by Thames and Hudson Limited; 48, taken from BLOOD, SWEAT AND TEARS, PHOTOGRAPHS FROM THE GREAT MINERS' STRIKE 1984-5, published by Artworker Books, and reproduced with the permission of Network Photographers, photograph by John Sturrock; 54, © Tom Carroll; 56, taken from SCOTSWOOD ROAD, © Jimmy Forsyth, published by Bloodaxe Books; 60, © Stockport Metropolitan Borough, courtesy of Stockport Museums and Art Gallery; 24, 66, taken from DOWN AND OUT: ORWELL'S PARIS AND LONDON REVISITED by Sandy Craig and Chris Schwarz, published by Penguin Books, 1984, illustration © Chris Schwarz; 68, courtesy of Magnum Photographs, photograph by Philip Jones Griffiths; 70, © Brian Shuel.

The lyrics for WAITING FOR ME PAY DAY are reproduced by permission of Opax Magazines plc; FOR CARLO is reproduced by permission of Robson Books and the lyrics for KING COTTON by Chappell Music Limited.

Whilst every effort has been made to trace copyright holders, this has not always been possible. The author and publishers would be glad to rectify any inaccuracies for future reprints.